ISCMEDICAL
Interview Skills Consulting

GP RECRUITMENT
STAGE 3

Role-play for
the GPST / GPVTS
Selection Centre

Author: George Lee

**MA (Cantab), MB BChir (Cantab),
MRCS (Ed), FRCS (Urol), FEBU**

Published by ISCMedical
Suite 434, Hamilton House, Mabledon Place, London WC1H 9BB
www.iscmedical.co.uk - Tel: 0845 226 9487

First edition (published in electronic form): October 2006
Second edition: October 2007

ISBN13: 978-1-905812-15-8
A catalogue record of this book is available from the British Library.

ISCMEDICAL
Interview Skills Consulting

INTRODUCTION

In this book, you will find 24 role-play scenarios that you will be able to practise with family, friends or colleagues. For each scenario, we have provided:

- **A brief for the candidate (the doctor): see Section 1 – starts p.5**
  You should read Section 1 only and no other section prior to the role play

- **A brief for a patient or third party: see Section 2 – starts p.31**
  This part can be played by anyone (friend, colleague, etc). The brief contains information that supplements the doctor's brief.

- **A suggested approach: see Section 3 – starts p.57**
  This includes key points to raise during the consultation and example phrases that you can use to enrich the content of your consultation. This should be read only after you have attempted the role play once.

For each scenario, you should allow yourself 5 minutes of preparation to read the scenario and plan your approach. Each consultation should last no more than 15 to 20 minutes.

Role plays are primarily about communication. Although you will obviously need some clinical knowledge to address some of the issues handled in each scenario, you should concentrate mostly on the communication aspect of each situation and show that you are able to demonstrate good listening skills and appropriate empathy.

Good luck with your preparation.

George Lee

TIPS FOR SUCCESS

Role plays concentrate essentially on the communication aspect of the consultation rather than your clinical abilities, although of course examiners will expect you to have a good basic knowledge of the clinical situation.

What are examiners testing?
Examiners will be looking for the following features:
- Building a rapport with the patient.
- Eliciting patient ideas, prior knowledge, concerns, etc. This includes dealing with psychosocial issues.
- Demonstrating confidence about the clinical situation.
- Explaining issues in a clear language, using appropriate sensitivity.
- Checking the patient's understanding.

How to tick the boxes
- Introduce yourself appropriately to the patient.
- Make sure that you listen attentively to what they are telling you. There may be clues that you need to pick up on and it will help you address their needs effectively.
- Make sure that you use simple language. Do not go over the top on clinical issues and ensure that you offer additional information in the form of leaflets, websites, etc. at the end of the consultation.
- Check the patient's understanding and address all his/her questions. If you do not know the answer, admit it and offer to find out (or to refer).
- Some scenarios will test your behaviour when confronted with a difficult situation that you may not be able to handle (e.g. a patient who endlessly repeats the same thing and does not really want to listen to you). Always remain civil but you can be assertive if need be.

Section 1

Doctor's Brief

1	**MISSED DIAGNOSIS**	
	Patient's Brief: Page 32	Suggested Approach: Page 58

You are a GP. You have been treating 55-year-old Mr Smith, who has been suffering from dyspepsia for the last two years. When you saw Mr Smith previously, he was slightly overweight and had no other complaints apart from minor symptoms suggestive of indigestion. At the time, Mr Smith had suggested that he might need "a scan of some sort", but you did not think that it was necessary based on his symptoms.

Three weeks ago, Mr Smith was admitted with a massive haematemesis. He spent one week in ITU and subsequently passed away. The post-mortem confirmed a metastatic gastric cancer, which eroded a major vessel. Mrs Smith is distraught and has made an appointment to discuss with you her concerns regarding her husband's death.

Your preparatory notes:

2	**DELAYED DIAGNOSIS**
	Patient's Brief: Page 33 Suggested Approach: Page 60

You are a Gastroenterology SHO and you looked after 61-year-old Mr Jones earlier in the year after he was admitted for persistent diarrhoea and abdominal pain. This was attributed to Irritable Bowel Syndrome. On discharge, his liver function tests (LFTs) were slightly abnormal, but you were not concerned since his symptoms had settled and he was otherwise fit and healthy. You suggested that he returned as an outpatient for repeat LFTs three months later.

Three months later the LFTs remained abnormal and you proceeded to investigate with an abdominal ultrasound scan. The scan showed a widespread liver metastasis. The patient knows the result and he thinks this could have been prevented if the ultrasound scan had been carried out three months earlier.

You are now seeing Mr Jones a few days after he has been informed of the diagnosis. He is clearly upset and blames you for not acting sooner.

Your preparatory notes:

3	GIVING A DIFFICULT DIAGNOSIS
	Patient's Brief: Page 34 Suggested Approach: Page 62

You are a Urology SHO. You have received a phone call from a radiographer with regard to a 28-year-old newly married man who noticed a testicular swelling and was referred for an ultrasound scan. The radiographer tells you that the results are suggestive of a tumour. The radiographer did not discuss the result with the patient, but asked the patient to go straight to your clinic.

It is a busy clinic that is already running over by an hour. The patient is anxious and suspects bad news. You have just 15 minutes to see the patient before you have to leave to assist in theatre. You will need to convince the patient to undergo urgent blood tests, sperm banking, a staging CT scan and urgent surgery. Demonstrate how you can do that effectively.

Your preparatory notes:

4	SEXUALLY TRANSMITTED INFECTION
	Patient's Brief: Page 35 Suggested Approach: Page 64

You are a GP. You are looking after Mr Morris, who is 27, is married and has a recurrent sexually transmitted infection. He discloses having had unprotected sexual intercourse with extramarital partners. His wife is a cleaner at your practice, but she is not one of your patients. You saw Mr Morris last week and suspected his genital lesion to be syphilis. The serology results confirm this diagnosis.

In the past you have encouraged Mr Morris to inform his wife of his sexually transmitted infections so that she could also have check-ups and be treated because of her contact with him. He has told you that he has been completely open with his wife, but you suspect he has not told her the whole story despite her getting adequate contact treatment from your colleagues and GU clinics. You are seeing the patient today to discuss his diagnosis and again to engage in partner notification. You also need to discuss with him issues surrounding safe sex. Given the high chance that he has passed the syphilis to his wife and that she will be positive when tested, you know that he can't put this down to a "water infection" this time and that he will need to be open with his wife.

Your preparatory notes:

9

5	**OCCUPATIONAL HEALTH**
	Patient's Brief: Page 36 Suggested Approach: Page 66

You are a GP and you are looking after Mr Davis, who is a junior doctor. He works at the local hospital as a surgical trainee. When you last saw him a couple of weeks ago, he was feeling lethargic and unwell. He informed you that he had had an unreported needlestick injury when treating an IV drug abuser four months before and that he was worried about the transmission of HIV.

You took blood, which came back as HIV seronegative but positive for Hepatitis C. He should have stopped "exposure-prone procedures" immediately, which would drastically limit his career in surgery. The patient knows the results of the blood test, but he is still working as a doctor at the local hospital.

You are seeing the patient today to discuss Hepatitis C treatment and whether he has informed Occupational Health.

Your preparatory notes:

6	**NEW HIV DIAGNOSIS**
	Patient's Brief: Page 37 Suggested Approach: Page 68

You are a GP. One of your patients, Sheila Andrews, is a single mother who works as a receptionist in your practice. She has been feeling lethargic and unwell recently. She is very honest with you and tells you about the break-up of a recent relationship, which "may be why she is feeling so down". She only knew this partner for a few months but he had to leave to go back to his family in Ghana.

As part of your investigations you included an HIV test, which came back positive. This is totally unexpected to the patient. She is worried about her health, career, income and childcare. She is also worried about the issue of confidentiality because she works in the same practice. You informed the patient of the diagnosis last week and you are seeing the patient today for the second time to discuss further issues.

Your preparatory notes:

7	ADHERENCE TO TREATMENT
	Patient's Brief: Page 38 Suggested Approach: Page 70

You are a medical SHO. Mr Harris is a young epileptic patient who recently had a second work-related injury following recurrent epileptic fits. For his job, the patient needs to drive a lot; you think that the nature of his work is not suitable for epileptic patients. You suspect poor adherence to his medication. You requested a test for his blood's phenytoin level, which is noted as undetectable, thereby confirming your suspicions.

You are seeing the patient to discuss the importance of the medication. Explore the type of work he does and whether the employer and DVLA have been informed regarding the diagnosis.

Your preparatory notes:

 **ISC**MEDICAL
Interview Skills Consulting

8	**SERIOUS COMPLICATION**
	Patient's Brief: Page 39 Suggested Approach: Page 72

One of your diabetic patients had a lipoma on his thigh that you removed as a minor operation in your surgery. The operation was complicated post-operatively by a wound and infection. Unfortunately, antibiotic treatment was delayed and the rare condition of necrotising fasciitis followed. The patient has since had extensive debridement and is very unwell in ITU. The prognosis is unclear.

The patient's family has read on the Internet about the link between flesh-eating bugs and diabetes. They are unhappy and have complained that this potential complication was not discussed with the patient prior to the operation. You have an appointment with the son to discuss the issues surrounding the consent and prognosis of his father.

Your preparatory notes:

Interview Skills Consulting

9	LATE COMPLICATION
	Patient's Brief: Page 40 Suggested Approach: Page 74

A 62-year-old patient who underwent a routine transurethral resection of prostate (TURP) six months ago is now incontinent of urine and has also experienced erectile dysfunction. He is now wearing incontinence pads and is having relationship problems with his wife because of all this.

Although the patient understood these to be the potential complications, he did not expect them to have such a major impact on his quality of life. He has seen the urologist, but has so far declined further treatment. He is frustrated, depressed and embarrassed about his conditions.

You are a GP. Your role is to explore the issues surrounding the complications and to offer necessary help.

Your preparatory notes:

Interview Skills Consulting

10   INTERNET MEDICINE

Patient's Brief: Page 41   Suggested Approach: Page 76

A 34-year-old lady would like to have laser treatment for an unsightly mole on her face. She has read on the Internet about a newly developed treatment for which there exists very little scientific data on its efficiency and safety. You have also read somewhere that the treatment itself may result in unfavourable scars.

The patient has asked you to refer her to a laser therapist. You are not keen to do so as you are worried that she might have unreasonable expectations. The patient is upset that her request is not being granted.

You are the GP. Your role is to explore the issues surrounding her request.

Your preparatory notes:

11	**RESOURCE RATIONING – IVF**
	Patient's Brief: Page 42 Suggested Approach: Page 78

A couple in their late twenties were declined IVF treatment for fertility due to limited funding. Subsequently, they found out that friends who are in their thirties and who live in another town were granted NHS funding for treatment. The friends have other medical issues that support their applications. The couple are upset and threaten to go to the media to expose this problem of "postcode lottery".

You are their GP. You are now seeing the wife and have to respond to her alarm and frustrations. You have to explain how the process of selection is based on clinical and geographical criteria.

Your preparatory notes:

12	**OBESITY AND ITS CONSEQUENCES**
	Patient's Brief: Page 43 Suggested Approach: Page 80

Mrs Peters is a clinically obese patient. She went to see an orthopaedic surgeon but, because she was overweight, she was denied a total hip replacement. Not only would surgery confer a high anaesthetic risk, but hip replacements in such patients usually result in higher complication rates and have a life span of less than one year.

Mrs Peters has attempted to lose weight many times but has failed. She is disappointed because she is taking a lot of pain killers for her hip pain and she is denied the operation that she badly needs.

You are the GP. Discuss these issues with the patient.

Your preparatory notes:

13 | COMPLICATIONS OF CHRONIC THERAPY
Patient's Brief: Page 44   Suggested Approach: Page 82

A young patient who suffers from chronic severe asthma has had recurrent courses of oral steroids over the last five years. He is now grossly overweight and has developed diabetes mellitus. Treatment has also led to avascular necrosis of the head of his left femur. He is in a lot of pain and was refused surgery due to his weight and diabetic co-morbidity.

You are the GP who started the steroids in consultation with the hospital specialists. The patient has come to see you to discuss his problems and particularly the unhappiness that the complications have caused him. You are expected to discuss the necessity of treatment and the unfortunate complications that he is experiencing.

Your preparatory notes:

Doctor's Brief

14	**FEAR OF CANCER**
	Patient's Brief: Page 45 Suggested Approach: Page 84

Mr Collins is 45 years old and his father recently died of prostate cancer at the age of 65. He is very concerned about his own risk of prostate cancer. He has come to see you for a PSA screening test.

His wife called you earlier and mentioned that he has lost a lot of weight and has not been eating well. He has also not been sleeping well and is waking very early each morning. Mr Collins was very close to his father.

Your role is to explore Mr Collins' concerns.

Your preparatory notes:

15	**LATE FAILURE OF VASECTOMY**	
	Patient's Brief: Page 46	Suggested Approach: Page 86

You carried out a vasectomy on a 45-year-old patient (Mr Jones) a year ago. He recently discovered his wife was pregnant and accused her of having an affair. The husband came to see you and you have carried out a sperm count. The results have come back positive. This is most likely due to delayed recannulation, which is very rare and was not discussed at the initial consent.

You are now seeing the husband to discuss the results of the sperm count and explain the condition of recannulation.

Your preparatory notes:

16 MIX-UP WITH RESULTS

Patient's Brief: Page 47   **Suggested Approach: Page 88**

Mrs Roberts, a 45-year-old woman, was informed that her lumpectomy from the breast confirmed a high-grade breast cancer and that the CT scan had demonstrated widespread metastasis. You saw her last week and told her the bad news. You have asked her to return with her family to discuss the poor prognosis.

You have received a phone call from the hospital today informing you that there was a mix-up of records due to clerical error. In fact, her breast lump was benign and the scan was normal.

You are now seeing the patient to discuss the good news with her.

Your preparatory notes:

17	**RESPONSE TO BEREAVEMENT**
	Patient's Brief: Page 48 Suggested Approach: Page 90

Jane Rover, a 27-year-old patient, has just lost her mother due to breast cancer at the age of 50. The type of breast cancer may be hereditary, although the risks are small. The patient's husband has made an appointment for you to see Jane. She has been very depressed due to her loss and has occasionally demonstrated suicidal intentions. The patient's husband has indicated that Jane wants to discuss prophylactic mastectomies with you.

You are seeing the patient today. She appears anxious and has asked you to refer her to a breast surgeon. She expresses the wish to have this surgery despite this small risk of cancer.

Your role is to discuss her bereavement, anxiety and these extreme measures of preventing breast cancer.

Your preparatory notes:

18 A SCEPTICAL PATIENT – MMR

Patient's Brief: Page 49   Suggested Approach: Page 92

A 24-year-old single mother, Alisha Silva, has refused to let her 5-year-old son Johnny have the Measles/Mumps/Rubella (MMR) combination vaccine. She is worried about the association being made between the MMR vaccine and autism. She has repeatedly expressed wishes to have the child vaccinated with three single vaccines, but this is not available on the NHS.

Alisha has made another appointment with you to demand that the single vaccines are made available under NHS care since she cannot afford this privately (she is on income support).

You are worried that her son may suffer devastating consequences if he does not have the vaccine. Your role is to convince the mother that the triple vaccine is safe.

Your preparatory notes:

Interview Skills Consulting

19	SELF-FUNDED TREATMENT
	Patient's Brief: Page 50 Suggested Approach: Page 94

Mrs Jenkins is 65 years old and has been suffering from rheumatoid arthritis for many years. Her condition is deteriorating and all the conventional treatments have failed. She found out about a recent medication that is undergoing trials, but has so far shown a very promising outcome. Recruitment to trials has come to an end and the outcome of the NICE review is awaited.

The only way for the patient to start the medication is self-funding and on a named prescription basis. As her GP, the patient has persuaded you to prescribe the medication on these terms. You went ahead with it, thinking that she had enough savings to cope with the associated expense.

The patient's son, Matthew Jenkins, has arranged to see you today. He is upset about the consequences that your approach is having on his mother. Discuss the issues with the patient's son.

Your preparatory notes:

20 | PRESUMED MALTREATMENT
Patient's Brief: Page 51   Suggested Approach: Page 96

Mrs Jones is an elderly lady who suffers from Alzheimer's disease and has been having recurrent falls. You are the Elderly Care SHO and you have witnessed, as well as treated, these falls on several occasions. In particular, at night she often gets confused and simply falls off her bed.

The patient's son has arranged to see you. He is concerned about his mother's bruises and about the possibility that she is being abused on the ward. He is also concerned about the lack of definitive action to reduce future incidences.

Your role is to reassure the patient's son that there are no suspicious circumstances surrounding the bruises. You also need to convince her son that all measures have been taken to reduce future recurrences.

Your preparatory notes:

21	**FRASER GUIDELINES**
	Patient's Brief: Page 52 Suggested Approach: Page 98

After long consideration, you have just referred Anna Roberts, a 15-year-old girl, for termination of pregnancy (TOP). She is Fraser competent and has agreed to start the oral contraceptive pill (OCP) after the termination. In accordance with the Fraser guidelines, you have encouraged her to discuss the TOP and OCP with her mother, but she has refused.

You received a phone call from Anna's mother one week after the termination of pregnancy. The mother, Mrs Roberts, suspects your involvement and has demanded to see you for an explanation.

Your preparatory notes:

22	**SUBSTANCE ABUSE**
	Patient's Brief: Page 53 Suggested Approach: Page 100

Mr Jackson is a 38-year-old man. Up until six months ago he had a good job at a local car factory, but was made redundant when the company relocated its production elsewhere. About four months ago, his wife left him and took their two young children with her. He is under considerable strain at the moment as she is filing for divorce and she is reluctant to let him see the children.

Looking through his notes, you see that he has attended the practice more frequently over the last few months with minor illnesses. He was prescribed a short course of temazepam on his last visit, but you notice that he had a couple of A&E attendances with blackouts attributed to alcohol excess.

He comes to you, today, seeking your help. Your task is to explore the nature of this visit and underlying issues, and to support his rehabilitation.

Your preparatory notes:

23	**SUPPORT FOR PARENTS**
	Patient's Brief: Page 54 Suggested Approach: Page 102

You have treated Clare Pisani, a 15-year-old girl who has had recurrent falls. You suspect that she has been bullied at school, but she denies it. You are concerned about this and would like to take this further.

You have arranged to see Clare and her mother to discuss these issues but Clare has refused to come along. Your role is to discuss your concerns with the mother.

Your preparatory notes:

24   PARENTAL SEPARATION & THE CHILD

Patient's Brief: Page 55   Suggested Approach: Page 104

You have recently seen Peter Jones, a 14-year-old boy who came and asked for Prozac®. He has symptoms of depression as well as low mood and he has lost interest in enjoyable activities. He also suffers from insomnia.

When you last saw Peter he mentioned that he was finding it hard to deal with the fact that his parents were separating. You have arranged to see his father or his mother without Peter being present in order to discuss your concerns.

Your preparatory notes:

Section 2

Patient's Brief

1	**MISSED DIAGNOSIS**
	Doctor's Brief: Page 6 Suggested Approach: Page 58

The context of the consultation

You are playing the role of Mrs Smith, whose husband has recently died. Mr Smith, who was 55 years old, had been suffering from dyspepsia for the past two years. He recently went back to his GP with no real complaint apart from minor symptoms suggestive of indigestion. At the time, your husband had suggested that he might need "a scan of some sort", but the GP did not think that it was necessary.

Three weeks ago, your husband was admitted to hospital because he was vomiting blood. He spent one week in ITU and subsequently passed away. The post-mortem confirmed a metastatic gastric cancer, which eroded a major vessel. You are understandably very distraught and you have made an appointment with your husband's GP to discuss your concerns regarding your husband's death.

Playing the role

Your husband has just died in a very unpleasant and prolonged ITU admission. You are grief-stricken and angry. Questions that you can throw at the GP to express your anger include:

- *Why was the wrong diagnosis made when you had been treating my husband for so long?*
- *Why did you refuse to do a check-up earlier? After all, my husband did ask for a scan!*
- *Who is responsible for my husband's death? Can I still trust you as my GP?*
- *Why did it have to happen to me? Why did he have to die so horribly? I hold you personally responsible for all this.*

On the other hand, you still need your GP to be available to you for support and to help you get through the trauma of your husband's death. You are searching for further answers as a way of expressing your sorrow, such as:

- *What can I do now that I have lost my husband?*
- *How am I going to manage financially and emotionally?*

Ensure that you get angry again towards the end. Give the GP a long chance to offer the possibility to make a complaint. If no offer is forthcoming after a while then ask *"How can I go about making a complaint?"*

2	**DELAYED DIAGNOSIS**
	Doctor's Brief: Page 7 Suggested Approach: Page 60

The context of the consultation

You are 61-year-old Mr Jones. Earlier in the year, you were admitted on a gastroenterology ward for persistent diarrhoea and abdominal pain. This was attributed to Irritable Bowel Syndrome. On discharge, your liver function tests (LFTs) were slightly abnormal, but the doctor was not overly concerned.

Three months later you returned for a follow-up appointment. The LFTs remained abnormal and the doctor arranged an abdominal ultrasound scan. The scan showed that you had liver cancer.

You are now seeing the doctor again a few days after you were informed of the diagnosis. You are clearly upset and blame the doctor for not acting sooner.

Playing the role

You have just been diagnosed as having metastatic cancer. You are angry and you are also still overcoming your shock. You want to blame someone for your condition. You think this could have been prevented if the ultrasound scan had been carried out three months earlier. In fact, you believe that an early scan would have made it possible to cure you. You will be asking the following:

- *What are these liver tests? Why bother doing the tests if you end up ignoring their results anyway?*
- *Why did you refuse to do anything when the LFTs were originally found to be abnormal?*
- *Why wasn't the scan done three months before? Surely it could have saved my life.*
- *Who is responsible for this death sentence? Can I still trust you doctors?*
- *How can I go about making a complaint?*

On the other hand, you need your doctor to be available to give you support and to help you to go through the treatment of cancer. You have many questions:

- *What is the origin of this cancer? Is this curable?*
- *What should I do now / next?*
- *How can I manage financially and emotionally?*
- *Will I suffer before I die?*

"ISCMEDICAL
Interview Skills Consulting

3	**GIVING A DIFFICULT DIAGNOSIS**
	Doctor's Brief: Page 8 Suggested Approach: Page 62

The context of the consultation

You are a 28-year-old newly married man. You recently noticed a swelling of one of your testicles for which you were referred to have an ultrasound scan at your local hospital. The radiographer did not tell you the results of the scan but, instead, he simply told you to go straight to the urology clinic. You are about to see the Urology SHO in clinic about this matter.

Playing the role

During the consultation, you must act very anxious. There are a number of issues that you need to address:

- ***Your anxiety and annoyance***

  You are annoyed because you are totally in the dark about what is going on. However, a couple of factors make you suspect bad news:
  - The referral to the urology clinic was fast-tracked
  - You noticed that the ultrasonographer got anxious about the scan results. In fact, you overheard the ultrasonographer talk to the urology SHO over the phone and you heard the word "cancer" – no one has realised that you overheard the conversation!

  You are very frustrated because you have waited all day, wanting someone to sit down with you to tell you everything. You are scared that you may have cancer, particularly since you overheard the ultrasonographer mention the word "cancer" to the SHO on the phone.

- ***The possibility of surgery***

  If the doctor suggests surgery, act scared and refuse it. Ask whether there are any alternatives. You are young and just married. You want to live a long life and to have children with your wife. You fear that a surgical intervention will make you unable to have a proper family life.

- ***Your fear of cancer***

  Although you have heard somewhere that testicular cancer has high cure rates, you are scared of cancer, chemotherapy, infertility and impotence. You are also worried that if nothing works you might die.

4	**SEXUALLY TRANSMITTED INFECTION**
	Doctor's Brief: Page 9 Suggested Approach: Page 64

The context of the consultation

You are Mr Morris, 27 years old and married. You have a recurrent sexually transmitted infection. In the past, you have admitted to your GP that you had unprotected sexual intercourse with extramarital partners. Your wife is a cleaner at the GP's practice but she is not a patient there.

In the past, your GP encouraged you to inform your wife of your sexually transmitted infections so that she could also have check-ups. You reassured the GP that you were completely open with your wife, though you have often mentioned to her that the symptoms were due to "water infection" rather than sexual infection following your promiscuity.

Last week you went to the GP because you had genital lesion. You are now back at the GP's to find out about the test results.

Playing the role

You have recently been unfaithful to your wife and you are aware that it was the wrong thing to do. There are a number of issues that you are worried about:

- *Your marriage*
  You still love your wife and would like to have counselling to resolve your marital issues. You would like to break the news gently to your wife yourself but you don't know how to approach the matter.

- *Confidentiality*
  You worry that your GP will tell your wife without your consent. You also worry that your GP may judge you and treat you suboptimally as a result.

- *The disease*
  During the consultation the GP will tell you that you have syphilis. You are very scared of syphilis. You don't know whether it is curable. You want to know whether you have transmitted the disease to the others. You worry about catching other diseases such as HIV.

5	## OCCUPATIONAL HEALTH
	Doctor's Brief: Page 10 Suggested Approach: Page 66

The context of the consultation

You are Mr Davis, a junior trainee surgeon. Four months ago, you got a needle-stick injury which prompted you to go to your GP in confidence. You told the GP that you had not reported the incident to the Trust. Tests showed that you were HIV-negative but that you had contracted Hepatitis C. You should normally have stopped carrying out any procedures that put patients at risk of contracting Hepatitis C from you but you are still working at the same hospital. You are now seeing the GP again to discuss the situation.

Playing the role

There are a number of issues that you want to discuss with the GP, including:

- ***Informing your employer***
  Despite advice from the GP, you have so far refused to inform the hospital of your condition because you are scared that you might lose your job. Be honest with the GP on this point. You have a mortgage and you are worried that, while receiving treatment, you will not be able to repay it.

- ***The impact on your career and your family***
  You are angry. You hate the fact that an IV drug user has maybe robbed you of your life while you were on duty. You had a great career and a loving family, and you are angry that everything has fallen apart.

- ***Hepatitis C and possible treatment options for Hepatitis C***
  You don't know much about Hepatitis C but you worry about the risk of having transmitted it to other patients and to your wife in the last four months. Ask the GP to give you more information.

- ***How you can make sure that your wife does not catch it from you***
  "What can I do to protect her?" - "Is there any way in which I can keep this hidden from her so that she doesn't worry?"

- ***Possible compensation***
  You want to make a claim for compensation, though you worry that it might take a long time and that the rewards are small.

6 — NEW HIV DIAGNOSIS

Doctor's Brief: Page 11   Suggested Approach: Page 68

The context of the consultation

You are Sheila Andrews, a receptionist at the GP surgery and also a patient there. You have recently terminated your relationship with a man who has now gone back to his native Ghana to be closer to his family; the relationship lasted only a few months.

Recently, you have been feeling down and you attributed your feelings to the recent break-up. However, last week the GP diagnosed you as HIV seropositive. You are now seeing the GP again to discuss further issues.

Playing the role

You must act as though you have heard a lot about HIV and AIDS but cannot really make sense of all the facts. Part of this role play is to encourage the GP to explain to you in simple terms what this is all about and what options are open to you. In particular, you do not understand the difference between HIV and AIDS. The new diagnosis has raised a number of worries:

- **The treatment**
  "Can this be treated? I have heard that people can die from AIDS and that it is a horrible death? Is it true?"
  "I have also heard that some people were treated with cocktails of antiviral drugs and that this might give you a normal life expectancy. Can you tell me more about it?"

- **Your child from a previous relationship (she is 5 years old)**
  Despite the fact that you may have contracted HIV after you had your child, you think that you may have passed it to her since.

- **You future**
  You worry about the effects of treatment, especially since you can't afford to take much time off work and lose income to support you and your child.

- **Confidentiality**
  One of your main worries is that, being a member of staff, your records are always exposed. You think you deserve the right to confidentiality. How will the GP handle this aspect?

7	ADHERENCE TO TREATMENT
	Doctor's Brief: Page 12 Suggested Approach: Page 70

The context of the consultation

You are a young marketing manager and you feel healthy most of the time. You are epileptic and your job frequently requires you to drive to different venues. You are under medication but you hate to take it because of the side effects, especially when it is mixed with alcohol; this stops you living your life. For that reason you sometimes "forget" to take it. Recently, you incurred a second work-related injury following recurrent epileptic fits. The GP now wants to discuss with you the importance of taking your medication and whether you should inform your employer and the DVLA about your condition.

Playing the role

You are angry, because you want to be normal like every other young man. Although you understand the importance of medical adherence, you sometimes just forget to take the tablets and want some help and support.

There are several important aspects that you want the GP to understand:
- You are worried about losing your job and income.
- You love to drive; it is important for your job and your social life. For that reason you have not notified your employer or the DVLA of your condition.
- You think it is very unfair that your condition should completely stop you from driving. You feel like you have lost your freedom.
- You don't see what is wrong with driving and being epileptic.

Possible phrases are:
- *You don't know what it's like to be the only one who can't drive.*
- *I'll be trapped without my car. My car is what makes me free to do what I want!*
- *Why can't I just do what I like, like my mates?*
- *I know I need the meds but I'd just like a break some time and it's so easy to slip up once in a while.*

When the GP tells you that you ought to notify the DVLA and your employer, ask whether this is compulsory and what would happen if you refused to do it (after all you don't want to risk losing your job).

8	**SERIOUS COMPLICATION**
	Doctor's Brief: Page 13 Suggested Approach: Page 72

The context of the consultation
Your father had a lipoma on his thigh, which was removed by a minor operation at the GP's surgery. Unfortunately, antibiotic treatment was delayed and the rare condition of necrotising fasciitis followed. Subsequently, your father has ended up in intensive care and is very ill.

You have complained to the GP that this possible complication was not discussed with your father or his family before the operation. You are now seeing the GP to obtain further details and discuss the issue of consent for the operation.

Playing the role
You are very worried that your father might die in the most awful conditions. There are several avenues that you need to pursue:

- *Information about your father's health*
  You are worried because you don't know the outcome of the complications. You have heard a lot of things on the news and on the Internet about flesh-eating bugs, but you are not entirely sure as to what the condition is and what your father's chances of recovery are. Ask the GP to give you more details in simple terms.

- *The GP's competence*
  You are angry because your GP carried out this "minor operation" that has gone wrong. You think he should have left it to the hospital rather than the GP surgery.
  "Are you in fact qualified to do these things outside the hospital?"
  "How could this thing happen? Couldn't you have prevented this?"

- *Consent and future plan*
  You think your father was not properly consented prior to the surgery and that therefore he was not made aware of a possible infection.
  "I thought that flesh-eating bug infection was a well-known complication for diabetic patients! Why wasn't my father warned of this?"
  "What are you going to do now?"

9 LATE COMPLICATION

Doctor's Brief: Page 14   Suggested Approach: Page 74

The context of the consultation

You are a 62-year-old male patient who underwent a routine transurethral resection of prostate (TURP) six months ago. As a result of the operation, you have become incontinent of urine, for which you have to wear incontinence pads. You are also experiencing erectile dysfunction, which is placing a strain on your relationship with your wife.

Before the operation you enjoyed a very active lifestyle. The potential risks were fully explained to you so you are not blaming anyone, but you think that you have made a mistake to go ahead with the surgery. You are now seeing the GP to address all these issues.

Playing the role

Your tone should be resigned, depressed and embarrassed, but not angry. You are not blaming anyone but your own poor decision making. There are a number of issues that you will need to discuss during the consultation:

- ***Your poor quality of life***
  You went ahead with the operation because you just wanted the "water-works" problems resolved but now you are incontinent and impotent. This is having a massive effect on your life.

- ***Your marriage and other problems***
  Your quality of life is so poor that you think your wife is going to leave you. You are waking up early each morning and are not sleeping well during the night. You have lost weight and aren't eating well. You are depressed and have had thoughts of suicide on several occasions (your GP does not know this). All this is making you very embarrassed and frustrated.

- ***Your refusal of further treatment***
  You have seen a urologist who put forward the idea of receiving further treatment but you refused because you were scared that it might make things worse. You can't remember what the urologist was proposing to do but if you could be reassured that further treatment could improve the situation then you may consider at least thinking about it.

10	**INTERNET MEDICINE**
	Doctor's Brief: Page 15 Suggested Approach: Page 76

The context of the consultation

You are a 34-year-old lady, with an unsightly mole on your face, which you would like to be removed. You have recently read on the Internet about a newly developed laser treatment and have come to your GP so that he can refer you to a laser therapist.

Playing the role

During the consultation you must appear unrealistically enthusiastic. Your mole is really letting you down and you are looking forward to the treatment to look your best again. Here are a number of factors that you will need to address when appropriate:

- ***Your attitude towards the mole***
  You are certain that the mole on your face is unsightly; it has bothered you for a while and you feel that everyone notices it and is disgusted by it. If the GP suggests that you may need psychological support or counselling, you should appear offended that he should consider that you have psychological problems.

- ***Your reasons for wanting laser therapy***
  You want to see a plastic surgeon but you are scared of surgery (your GP does not know that you are scared of surgery). You feel that the right compromise will be using the laser, as this is not surgery.

- ***Your knowledge of the laser treatment***
  You know nothing specific about the procedure or its complications. You have simply read reviews in glossy magazines, which talk about miraculous results. If the GP mentions that there is a lack of supporting evidence in favour of laser treatment, keep referring to the testimonials that you read in the magazines in a bid to impress him.

- ***Your attitude towards the GP and doctors***
  You suspect that your GP will not refer you to the laser therapist because of costs and that he won't hear you out. You are willing to pay for it yourself. You did not know that laser or beauty therapists are not doctors.

.

41

11	**RESOURCE RATIONING – IVF**	
	Doctor's Brief: Page 16	Suggested Approach: Page 78

The context of the consultation

You are a female patient in your late twenties and have been very disappointed with the lack of results after three years of trying for a baby. Due to limited financial resources, your request for IVF treatment was refused, which has left you disappointed. You cannot afford the treatment otherwise.

Recently, you found out that your friends, who live on the other side of town, had their IVF approved. You are now seeing the GP to discuss this problem.

Playing the role

You were disappointed to find out that your application for IVF had been rejected, but finding out that your friends' application was accepted because they live in a different area has left you very bitter. You must act very despondent and cynical, as well as angry.

During the consultation, you should raise the following points:

- **_The different verdicts_**
  You do not understand why people are treated differently. Your friends have not given you any specific information about their case but you would like your GP to find out why their application was accepted and why yours was not.

- **_Your anger towards this injustice_**
  You think that the whole thing is related to your postcode. Tell the GP that you will expose this postcode lottery to the media if you cannot get the treatment that you feel you deserve.

- **_Your marriage_**
  Trying for a baby for so long without results has put a strain on your marriage. Finding out that you live in the "wrong area" has just made things worse. You are holding the NHS responsible for all of this.

12 | OBESITY AND ITS CONSEQUENCES
Doctor's Brief: Page 17   **Suggested Approach: Page 80**

The context of the consultation
You are playing the role of Mrs Peters, a clinically obese patient. Because of your obesity, you have been denied a total hip replacement. In the past you have attempted many times to lose weight, without much success. Your hip is hurting a lot, and as a result you are taking many painkillers.

Playing the role
You are really annoyed with the medical profession because you are not getting the hip replacement that you really need. There are several issues that you want to raise:

- ***The doctors' attitude***
  You know that you are overweight but you found the surgeons insulting and stereotyping. You have tried to lose weight but have failed miserably. This is not due to lack of will but it is just very hard to do and the surgeons don't seem to appreciate that.

- ***The refusal***
  You are angry as you have been a taxpayer all your life and you feel that you deserve the treatment. You think that the operation was refused for financial reasons and you want some answers from the GP about the exact reason (you are unaware of the fact that the life span of the artificial hip is shortened in an obese patient).

- ***The lack of support from the GP***
  You do not think your GP offers you enough support to help you lose weight. You are also in a lot of pain. You are getting disturbing side effects of the painkillers such as constipation. You don't think your GP cares.

13	COMPLICATIONS OF CHRONIC THERAPY
	Doctor's Brief: Page 18 Suggested Approach: Page 82

The context of the consultation

You are young and have been affected by chronic severe asthma for a long time. You have had many visits to A&E and a couple of ITU admissions. Your GP prescribed steroids in consultation with the hospital specialists. The steroid treatment has now ruined your life. It has destroyed your hip and you have become diabetic and overweight. In addition, because you have become obese, you have been refused surgery for a hip replacement. You are seeing the GP to discuss the treatment and its complications.

Playing the role

During the consultation there are a number of messages that you would like to pass on to the GP:

- *The steroid treatment*
  You are in pain and depressed as a result of the obesity, diabetes and the hip problems that have developed as a result of the steroids. You want to stop the steroids immediately and hope that your life will revert to normal (you do not know that you can't stop your medication instantly). You think your GP has ruined your life by starting you on steroid treatment.

- *The refusal of hip replacement surgery*
  You are angry that you are being denied a hip replacement on account of your obesity. You think it is grossly unfair, particularly as the obesity is due to the steroids that were prescribed by the GP in the first place.
  "The NHS is really inconsistent. It is the NHS that made me obese in the first place and now they are using my obesity to deny me further treatment."

- *An uncertain future*
  You find that the future is bleak and that there are not many options open to you. You are constantly in pain and always seem to be taking one pill or another. You can't see the situation getting any better unless you have hip replacement surgery and stop the steroids straight away.

14	**FEAR OF CANCER**
	Doctor's Brief: Page 19 Suggested Approach: Page 84

The context of the consultation

You are playing the role of Mr Collins, aged 45. Your father has recently died of prostate cancer at the age of 65. You were close to him, and you are saddened and mourning this loss.

Your wife has contacted the GP because you have lost a lot of weight and have not been eating well. You are waking up very early in the morning. You have come to see the doctor to see if you can get screening for prostate cancer.

Playing the role

During the consultation you must act very worried. There are several factors that worry you:

- **Prostate cancer**
  There are a number of factors that make you think that you have also got prostate cancer. As well as the weight loss and lack of appetite, you also very frequently often feel the need to have a wee. This is similar to what your father experienced before his diagnosis. You suspect you have got early prostate cancer. You are scared and confused. You are not sure whether it is worthwhile finding out more.

- **Depression**
  You have been deeply affected by your father's death but also by the risk that you may have cancer yourself. You are so anxious that you have become depressed. You can't say for sure whether the depression is actually linked to your bereavement or solely to your fear of cancer – you just feel depressed. You have no suicidal thoughts though (only deny suicidal thoughts if the GP specifically enquires about it).

- **Information**
  You want the GP to educate you about prostate cancer a bit more. There are a number of issues that you want to find out about, including how a possible cancer can be detected and what the future holds for you if you have prostate cancer. Let him talk to you and only prompt if necessary.

ISCMEDICAL
Interview Skills Consulting

15	LATE FAILURE OF VASECTOMY
	Doctor's Brief: Page 20 Suggested Approach: Page 86

The context of the consultation

You are Mr Jones, a 45-year-old male patient who had a vasectomy a year ago. Recently, your wife announced that she was pregnant and, in view of your operation, you suspect that she has been having an affair. You went to see your GP, who organised a sperm count. You are now seeing the GP, who will reveal the results of the sperm count to you.

Playing the role

- *Dealing with the test results*

  During the consultation, the GP will reveal that the sperm count is positive. When he announces the results, you are very surprised because you thought that a vasectomy meant you would effectively be sterile. The GP will tell you that this is most likely due to a rare condition called "recannulation". You must make sure that he explains the condition to you in simple terms. Once he has given his explanation, you should act angry because none of this was mentioned before the surgery, when consent was sought from you for the procedure. In fact you might want to threaten to make an official complaint.

- *Your wife's alleged affair*

  You are also sorry and ashamed that you have accused your wife of having an affair. You thought you should have trusted her more. You are blaming the doctors for the marital difficulties that this has led to.

- *The prospect of another child*

  More importantly you are now scared of the prospect of another child in the family. You already have three young children and you don't think you can afford another child. You are not sure about abortion as you are Catholic and you think it may risk your wife's health (your GP does not know about these issues; make sure you place them in the consultation at an appropriate time).

46

16 MIX-UP WITH RESULTS

Doctor's Brief: Page 21   Suggested Approach: Page 88

The context of the consultation
You are Mrs Roberts, a 45-year-old woman. Recently, you had a lump removed from your breast, which was confirmed as a high-grade breast cancer. A CT scan revealed widespread metastasis. Last week you saw the GP, who broke the bad news to you. You are now seeing the GP again to discuss the poor prognosis.

Playing the role
During the consultation the GP will tell you that he has received a phone call from the hospital, announcing that there had been a mistake and that, in fact, your lump was benign and that the scan was normal. There has simply been a clerical error. There are a number of issues that you will need to raise:

- **Dealing with the good news**
  You are of course relieved that you haven't got cancer, but you have lost faith in the hospital. You worry that they may make the mistakes again. You can't see yourself going back there.

- **Anxiety resulting from the diagnosis**
  For the past week you have been anxious about the diagnosis. You have been afraid of dying and there were times when you wondered if you could put up with all this. If asked by the GP about suicidal thoughts, mention that you never really seriously contemplated suicide but the thought did vaguely cross your mind.

- **Family problems arising from the diagnosis**
  You are angry because you have made arrangements to travel the world before you die and have also dealt with some sensitive family issues that you wouldn't have confronted if you thought you were going to live. This has created a lot of tension at home. Sorting out your will has led to some violent family arguments and you blame the doctors for this mess.

- **Possible action**
  At some stage in the consultation you should ask the GP what he and you can do about the mix-up. Is it possible to complain?

17	**RESPONSE TO BEREAVEMENT**
	Doctor's Brief: Page 22 Suggested Approach: Page 90

The context of the consultation
You are playing the role of Jane Rover, a 27-year-old woman whose mother has just died of breast cancer at the age of 50.

You know this disease can be hereditary and you do not want your children to experience such bereavement in the future. You think that the best way for you to avoid getting breast cancer is to have both breasts removed as a precaution (prophylactic mastectomies). Your husband has booked an appointment with the GP to discuss this.

Playing the role
During the consultation, you should appear very anxious. There are three issues that you will need to make the GP aware of:

- *Your bereavement*
  You and your mother were like sisters. You are very depressed and you have thought of "ending it all" (make sure you emphasise your suicidal tendencies). You simply cannot cope with your loss and you need help!

- *Your anxiety and fear of getting the cancer yourself*
  You have read that the cancer that your mother had <u>may</u> be hereditary (this is only a possibility, not a certainty) and you are scared for your future and that of your children. What happened to your mother frightens you. This stops you from leading a normal life.

- *Your wish for a double mastectomy*
  You do not want to take any chances. You simply can't put your children through what you went through yourself and the only way to take out the risk of getting breast cancer yourself is by having both breasts removed as a precaution. You want your GP to refer you to a breast surgeon.

During the consultation, the GP should suggest that a double mastectomy is a rather drastic way of dealing with the risk. Let him offer alternative suggestions (screening, early detection and cure). Let him get to that stage by himself. If he does not, then ask: *"You must think I am mad. If you think that I am over the top, what do you think I should do?"*

18 — A SCEPTICAL PATIENT – MMR

Doctor's Brief: Page 23   Suggested Approach: Page 92

The context of the consultation

You are playing the role of Alisha Silva, a single mother. Your son Johnny is 5 years old and means the world to you. You have investigated whether your son should be vaccinated with the Measles/Mumps/Rubella (MMR) combination vaccine. But the bad press that the vaccine has received has put you off.

You know that the NHS will only fund the combined MMR vaccine and that if you want to have all three vaccines done separately then you will need to pay for it yourself. You are now seeing your GP to convince him that your son should receive all three vaccines separately on the NHS.

Playing the role

During the consultation, you should appear anxious You should use the following opinions and questions as appropriate.

- **The MMR vaccine**

  You have read a lot of newspaper cuttings but actually do not understand most of them. You have heard that the MMR vaccine leads to autism and you don't want this to happen to your son. As a result, you believe that the best option is either to have the single vaccines or no vaccine at all. This should prompt the GP to provide some explanations. Make sure that you probe into everything that the GP tells you. Questions you can use include:

  "You say that MMR does not lead to autism. Why does every newspaper say the contrary then?"

  "What would happen if my child caught measles, mumps or rubella?"

  "Why is the combined vaccine better than the independent vaccines?"

- **Funding for the vaccine**

  You think that the single vaccines have been refused to you because the NHS is discriminating against single mothers and people on income support. Basically your low income means that you simply cannot afford to get the vaccines done privately. You also think that doctors just fob you off with jargon, thinking that you are stupid and knowing you won't understand them.

In order to test the GP's creativity, resist the GP's pressure and do not give in. Be argumentative, but not aggressive.

19 SELF-FUNDED TREATMENT

Doctor's Brief: Page 24   Suggested Approach: Page 94

The context of the consultation

You are playing the role of Matthew Jenkins. Your mother, Mrs Jenkins, is 65 years old and has been suffering from rheumatoid arthritis for many years. Her condition has been deteriorating for some time and all conventional treatments have failed. Recently, she was advised by her GP that a new drug was being trialled and that she could get hold of it on a named prescription basis, but only if she funded the treatment herself. As a result your mother has sold her flat to pay for the treatment (the GP does not know this). You are angry and you have requested an appointment with the GP.

Playing the role

During the consultation, you should act angry (though still reasonable enough for the GP to be able to talk to you). You will want to address the following:

- **Your mother's disastrous situation**
  You feel that the GP has conned your mother into selling her flat. You are even more upset that, after spending this money, she is now worse off.
  "You may not know this, but she has sold her flat and she has nothing left!"

- **The GP's negligence**
  You feel that the GP went ahead with the prescription without checking properly that your mother could afford it. As a result, you feel that the GP has mistreated your mother and you are threatening to take this further, possibly to the GMC.

- **Your mother's condition**
  You want to find out more about your mother's condition and the circumstances that led the GP to make such a decision. The GP should refuse to give you any information. Try to push the GP to breach confidentiality. If he refuses to tell you anything (rightly), you should sound upset and use sentences such as:
  "I can see that you are obviously trying to hide things from me in the same way that I suspect you might have hidden them from my mother."
  "Do you not think that enough damage has been done already? I am here to help my mother get out of the disastrous situation she finds herself in and the least you could do is work with me to sort this mess out."

50

20 | PRESUMED MALTREATMENT
Doctor's Brief: Page 25　　　　Suggested Approach: Page 96

The context of the consultation
You play the role of Mr Jones, whose mother (Mrs Jones) is elderly and suffers from Alzheimer's disease. Your mother has had several stays in hospital where she acquired a large number of bruises. Your mother tells you that the bruises are due to falls but you believe that this may be linked to abuse on the ward. You have arranged to see the SHO in Elderly Care to discuss your concerns.

Playing the role
You should act upset and very concerned. There are a number of issues that you wish to address with the GP, as follows:

- **_The bruising_**
  You are upset that your mother is bruised. This has now happened on several occasions. This is of great concern, particularly as your mother cannot fend for herself. You have read about nurses abusing elderly patients and think this has happened to her. When the SHO reassures you that the bruises are due to witnessed falls, you should not believe him straight away. Phrases that you can use include:
  "How can you be sure that all bruises are accounted for?"
  "I don't mean to be rude but perhaps you are also part of this conspiracy?!"

- **_Your mother's future safety_**
  You think the hospital isn't doing enough to protect her safety. You want reassurance that measures are in place to make sure that your mother is fully safe.
  "Is there any record of the falls? Can I talk to some of the witnesses?"
  "What does the hospital do to make sure that patients do not fall?"
  "How does the hospital make sure that it learns from past experience?"

- **_Formal complaint_**
  Despite all the reassurances, you are still not totally convinced. You really want to make a formal complaint about the events so that a full investigation will be made.

ISCMEDICAL
Interview Skills Consulting

21	**FRASER GUIDELINES**	
	Doctor's Brief: Page 26	Suggested Approach: Page 98

The context of the consultation

You are playing the role of Mrs Roberts, the mother of a 15-year-old girl called Anna. You suspect that Anna has just had a termination of a pregnancy. She is refusing to tell you anything, which makes you even more suspicious. Having read her diary, you note that she made an appointment with the GP a week ago and you suspect that the GP has something to do with it. You have booked an appointment with the GP to discuss your concerns about the situation.

Playing the role

The situation has left you worried, confused and helpless. During the consultation, try to be emotional to see if the GP can be influenced by your emotions. During the consultation, you should raise the following issues:

- ### The abortion

  You are almost certain that Anna has had an abortion. You want your GP to confirm this so that you have a chance of being able to deal with the problem directly with your daughter.

- ### Your fear of sexual abuse

  You are worried that your child had been sexually abused and are keen to help her. You want to protect her but you feel powerless. Keep asking the GP for information. For example: *"I can see why you may not want to tell me whether Anna had an abortion, but as a mother I need to know if she is suffering in any way so that I can help her. Does she have any personal problems that I need to know about?"*

- ### The role of the GP

  You feel betrayed by the GP. You think your GP is hiding something from you and you feel let down. You cannot understand why the GP cannot involve the parents in the decision making process for children under the age of 16. And you certainly can't understand why the GP won't give you a chance to make a difference to Anna's life by telling you what is going on.

- ### Anna's maturity

  The GP will tell you that, despite being 15 years old, Anna is mature enough to make her own decisions. Question this – Anna can be a bit dim!

22	**SUBSTANCE ABUSE**
	Doctor's Brief: Page 27 Suggested Approach: Page 100

The context of the consultation

You are playing the role of 38-year-old John Jackson. Until six months ago you had a good job at a local car factory, but you were made redundant when the company relocated its production elsewhere. About four months ago your wife left you and took your two young children with her. You are under considerable strain at the moment as she is filing for divorce and she is reluctant to let you see the children. You are seeing your GP to discuss how this is affecting you.

Playing the role

You should act resigned and depressed. During your discussion with the GP you will need to raise the following issues when prompted:

- **Your cry for help**

  You really want your GP to give you some sleeping pills. You have gone to your GP frequently in the last few months but you don't get much help. The last doctor thought that you needed help getting to sleep and gave you some sleeping tablets. You think this may be best for you since when you sleep you forget. If the GP is hesitant or reluctant, ask him why. After all, the previous doctor prescribed them easily. You can push the doctor on this. Ultimately, however, you are happy to consider any option to help you get out of the hole that you are falling into.

- **Your personal situation**

  You feel that your skills were very specific to your old job, that you are now useless and can't be trained in anything else. About four months ago your wife left you taking your two young daughters with her. She claims that you cannot support them anymore and she has since moved in with another man. You miss your daughters greatly and you are currently going through divorce proceedings.

- **Your alcohol problem**

  Since your wife left you, the only comfort you have had has been alcohol. You were never a big drinker. It started with a few whiskies but now it's more like a bottle a night. You have blacked out a few times in public and been taken to hospital but they quickly discharged you. You have wanted to get help for some time but you don't know where from.

ISCMEDICAL
Interview Skills Consulting

23	**SUPPORT FOR PARENTS**
	Doctor's Brief: Page 28 Suggested Approach: Page 102

The context of the consultation

You are playing the role of Mrs or Mr Pisani. You have a 15-year-old daughter, Clare. The GP has asked to see you and your daughter to discuss a number of issues but your daughter has refused to come with you.

Playing the role

You suspect your child has been bullied in school and you suspect that this may be what the GP wants to talk to you about. During the consultation, you will need to address the following points. Wait until you are prompted, but if you are not then introduce the elements yourself.

- *The bullying*

  You have had concerns about your daughter for some time. She has become very quiet and refuses to talk about what she does at school. You have noticed that some of her possessions have gone missing and occasionally you have also noticed that she has been stealing small sums of money from you. Her performance at school has been declining and she is constantly covered in bruises, which she puts down to falls that she incurs regularly.

- *Your fear of being judged*

  You are worried that your GP might be judgemental because you have done nothing so far or that he feels your child comes from a broken home. You worry that you will be labelled as a bad parent.

- *Your lack of direction*

  You don't know who to turn to and how to deal with the situation. You are lost and would like some guidance and support. You know that you need your daughter to open up but you don't know how to go about it.

- *Your fears for your daughter*

  You have absolutely no idea what is going through your daughter's mind at present and this scares you. You have read many articles about teenagers committing suicide over bullying and you really would like to be able to do something before it is too late.

Patient's Brief

24   PARENTAL SEPARATION & THE CHILD
Doctor's Brief: Page 29   Suggested Approach: Page 104

The context of the consultation
You are the father/mother of 14-year-old Peter Jones. Peter's GP has asked you to come and see him to discuss issues relating to your child, though he has not explicitly mentioned what these issues are. You are in the middle of a difficult separation from Peter's mother/father. You do not know at the time of the consultation that your son has visited the GP previously because he was finding it difficult to handle the separation.

Playing the role
During the consultation, you should play the role in a fairly relaxed manner, in other words not overly concerned by the issues raised by the GP.

- **Your child**
  You suspect that your child has not been himself lately but you think this is a phase and that he will overcome it with time. You suspect the consultation with the GP is about the child's recent unhappiness.

- **Your own situation**
  You are really struggling to cope with your marital breakdown and therefore you feel that you cannot do much to help your child. You feel that, if help is needed, it can't possibly come from you. In particular, you feel that your wife/husband should take an equal share of responsibility in sorting out this mess.

- **Your fear of being judged**
  You are worried that your GP might be judgemental. You worry that you will be labelled as a bad parent.

- **Your lack of direction**
  You are lost and would like some guidance and support with your own separation. You also need guidance to help you deal with your son's unhappiness.

Section 3

Suggested Approach

1	**MISSED DIAGNOSIS**
	Doctor's Brief: Page 6 Patient's Brief: Page 32

Key points to cover	**Example phrases**
Listen actively to Mrs Smith's concerns: • Misdiagnosis • Traumatic death from a bleeding cancer • Impact of this bereavement	
Demonstrate empathy: • Put yourself in Mrs Smith's place • Understand her loss and anger	*"I understand that you are upset and disappointed..."* *"I can sense anger and loss..."*
Check Mrs Smith's understanding of the reasons for the missed diagnosis	*"Do you understand why we did not suspect cancer in the first place?"*
Apologise for the missed diagnosis	*"I'm sorry for your loss and the way you are feeling right now"*
Give explanations appropriate to her level of understanding and interest	*"I hope you understand that all his symptoms did not indicate cancer."* *"Is there anything more that I can explain?"*
Offer support and continuity of care	*"I hope to continue to give you support and care to overcome this difficult period"*

Key points to cover (continued)

Example phrases (continued)

Give Mrs Smith the opportunity to lodge a complaint if conflict continues

"Of course, if you still feel very strongly about all of this, we can put you in touch with our patient liaison team who are independent of doctors and can take things further."

Ask if there are further questions and close (by scheduling a follow-up if appropriate)

ISCMEDICAL
Interview Skills Consulting

2	DELAYED DIAGNOSIS	
	Doctor's Brief: Page 7	Patient's Brief: Page 33

Key points to cover	Example phrases
Listen actively to Mr Jones's concerns: • His anger at the delayed diagnosis • His fear of the cancer	
Demonstrate empathy: • Put yourself in Mr Jones's place • Understand his fear and anger	*"I sympathise with your shock and concerns with the diagnosis of cancer"* *"I can sense your anger and disappointment towards me"*
Check Mr Jones's understanding of the reasons for the delay in the diagnosis and that an early scan wouldn't have led to a cure	*"I hope you understand that the abnormal liver test does not warrant an immediate ultrasound scan, and that having a scan three months before would not necessarily have made a great deal of difference"*
Explore his understanding of the diagnosis and explain in simple terms what is planned to happen next	
Offer support and continuity of care	*"I think it is time for us to move forward and find out the origin of the cancer, so that we can ask the specialist to treat you accordingly"*
Ask if there is anything further he wishes to clarify and offer a meeting with him and other family members if desired	

Key points to cover (continued)	Example phrases (continued)
Offer to tell Mr Jones how to lodge a complaint if conflict continues	*"I hope our conversation has clarified any misunderstandings. However, if you still feel very strongly about the delay in the ultrasound, we can always put you in touch with someone who can take this concern further"*
Offer the opportunity to take information leaflets or details of support groups if appropriate	
Ask if there are further questions and close (by scheduling a follow-up if appropriate)	

Interview Skills Consulting

3	**GIVING A DIFFICULT DIAGNOSIS**
	Doctor's Brief: Page 8 Patient's Brief: Page 34

Key points to cover   **Example phrases**

Listen actively to the patient's concerns: *"I understand you are*
- The shock of the diagnosis of cancer   *completely shocked by this*
- The degree of uncertainty at this stage   *unexpected abnormal result"*
- The worry about treatment
- Concerns about fertility and sexual
  function
- His prognosis

Demonstrate empathy:
- Put yourself in the patient's place
- Understand his fears and concerns

Make sure that the patient understands the   *"I know you are still in shock. I*
necessity for early surgery   *hope you understand that early*
                                                 treatment can make a
                                                 difference, therefore early
                                                 surgery is crucial"

                                                 "I know the word cancer has
                                                 been mentioned and indeed we
                                                 are concerned with the cancer
                                                 at present. However, I think the
                                                 right approach would be to carry
                                                 out the surgery as soon as
                                                 possible so that we can confirm
                                                 the diagnosis early and initiate
                                                 treatment appropriately"

Make sure that the patient understands that
the cure rate for the condition is high

Key points to cover (continued)	Example phrases (continued)
Explore his understanding of the diagnosis and explain in simple terms what is planned to happen next	
Ask if there is anything further he wishes to clarify – check his understanding. Offer the patient the opportunity to return later to discuss the treatment and prognosis with his family	*"Do you understand our conversation so far, or would you like to return with a member of family for further discussion?"*
Offer support and continuity of care	*"I know that you are scared and concerned. I would like you to know that we can give you all the support you may need"*
Offer the opportunity to take information leaflets or details of support groups if appropriate	
Ask if there are further questions and close (by scheduling a follow-up if appropriate)	

4	**SEXUALLY TRANSMITTED INFECTION**
	Doctor's Brief: Page 9 Patient's Brief: Page 35

Key points to cover	**Example phrases**
Listen actively to Mr Morris' concerns: ▪ The concern or lack of concern over the diagnosis of syphilis ▪ Risk of HIV transmission ▪ Relationship issues	*"I can see that you regret what you have done. However, for your health and in the best interests of your family you have a responsibility to tell them about this"*
Make sure that the patient understands that the syphilis can be eradicated, but that he and his wife need to be treated	*"We can move forward now by doing things that are for the best..."*
Encourage the patient to take an HIV test (but do not coerce him!)	*"If you have been exposed to some of these infections, there is a good chance you may have been exposed to others. For that reason, I would suggest that it would be wise to have an HIV test also"*
Demonstrate a non-judgemental attitude: ▪ Avoid using moralistic words like "right and wrong, shame or guilt" ▪ Make it known that it is the patient's health not the "ins and outs" of their private life that concerns you	*"I hope you realise that I am talking about these things because, in the long term, I want to keep you and your partner in good health, and I don't think any differently about you as one of my patients"*
Offer support and continuity of care	

Key points to cover (continued)	Example phrases (continued)
Explore his understanding of the diagnosis and explain in simple terms what is planned to happen next	*"I understand the dilemma and difficulties that you are facing now. As your doctor, I am prepared to be the person to talk to and support both of you"*
Be prepared to be challenged by the patient's wife for not informing her of the past STIs	*"I expect she may be upset or perhaps angry in the first instance, but we really need to resolve this very difficult problem as soon as possible"*
Offer the opportunity to take information leaflets or details of support groups if appropriate	
Ask if there are further questions and close (by scheduling a follow-up if appropriate)	

5	**OCCUPATIONAL HEALTH**	
	Doctor's Brief: Page 10	Patient's Brief: Page 36

Key points to cover

Listen actively to the patient's concerns:
- The diagnosis of Hep C
- Concern about career
- Concern about transmission of the virus in previous patients
- Concern about treatment of Hep C
- Concern about compensation

Demonstrate empathy:
- Put yourself in the patient's place
- Understand his fears and concerns

Make sure that the patient understands that he MUST stop any work that can put patients at risk. He must also inform occupational health immediately

Explain that occupational health is a confidential service despite being within the hospital and they may be able to assess his career options to determine what work he still may be able to do (non-invasive / laparoscopic?)

Example phrases

"As part of your job it means that you may be exposed to illnesses not due to any fault of your own. This is an unfortunate event and you will have to face it and get it treated. Can we discuss your concerns?"

"I can imagine what issues are going through your mind, like your career and treatments. It must be a difficult time for you"

"I'm worried that you're still doing work that may put patients at risk. I'm sure you understand our duties as doctors towards our patients. I must tell you to stop any work like this and to inform occupational health asap"

"I know this is difficult for you to confront and there are lots of things at stake, but what I also know is that it isn't the end of your career and that occupational health are there for you as much as for other patients. They will find out what options are open to you. They will also treat the situation with full confidentiality"

Key points to cover (continued)   **Example phrases (continued)**

You have the authority to override and reinforce the matter. You may breach confidentiality for the protection of other patients

"I will give you the opportunity to make contact with occupational health, but, if I find out that you don't and you continue to put patients at risk, you do know that I may have to pass this information on to others to prevent harm to patients?"

Remind him of the potential for treatment i.e. the referral to hepatology

Address issues regarding compensation but tread carefully

"I fully understand how angry you might feel about all of this and how you would want to get some compensation. We can make enquiries with occupational health. If you followed hospital policy when the accident first happened then there may be something they can do, but I can't make any promises right now"

Offer the opportunity to take information leaflets or details of support groups if appropriate

Ask if there are further questions and close (by scheduling a follow-up if appropriate)

6	**NEW HIV DIAGNOSIS**
	Doctor's Brief: Page 11 Patient's Brief: Page 37

Key points to cover   **Example phrases**

Listen actively to Ms Andrews' concerns:
- On diagnosis and treatment of HIV
- About her child's HIV status
- About her income and childcare
- About the protection of confidentiality

Demonstrate empathy:
- Put yourself in the patient's place
- Understand her fear and concerns

Explore her understanding of the diagnosis and explain in simple terms what is planned to happen next:
- Difference between HIV and AIDS
- The life expectancy for a HIV patient is high with early treatment
- The need to do baseline investigations to assess how well she is
- Explain that her acquisition may be recent and so her child is likely negative but the child can be tested to be sure

"From our conversation, I sense regrets and fears about the contraction of HIV. However, if we look to the future you may know that the modern treatments for HIV can help to keep people well for a long time and they can live active lives"

Offer support and continuity of care, but offer the opportunity to transfer her care to another practice to protect her confidentiality and explain that specialist care can be confidential at a GU unit.

"Although HIV will have a life-changing impact on your life and your child's life, we must work together to get you healthy and also fully protect your confidentiality at the same time"
"My role as your doctor is to support you physically and emotionally. I hope to help you overcome this difficult period"

Key points to cover (continued)   **Example phrases (continued)**

Offer to investigate the options of income
support and childcare

Offer the opportunity to take information
leaflets or details of support groups if
appropriate

Ask if there are further questions and close
(by scheduling a follow-up if appropriate)

7	**ADHERENCE TO TREATMENT**	
	Doctor's Brief: Page 12	Patient's Brief: Page 38

Key points to cover	**Example phrases**
Listen actively to the patient's concerns: ▪ Diagnosis and treatment of epilepsy ▪ Isolation living with the diagnosis ▪ Restrictions to working and social life ▪ Importance to keep driving	*"Tell me how all this affects you"* *"How do you feel this has changed your life?"*
Demonstrate empathy: ▪ Put yourself in the patient's place ▪ Show understanding of the life he leads	*"I can see this really has got to you"* *"From what you say you must be pretty frustrated with things"*
Convey with clarity: ▪ The necessity to inform the employer ▪ The duty to inform the DVLA either by him or, if not, by you ▪ The importance of adherence to medication ▪ Referral to neurologist for treatment and guidance ▪ Your authority to breach confidentiality if you think the condition can cause the patient and others harm	*"I know you have reasons for wanting to continue to drive but I have an obligation to encourage you to tell the DVLA. If you don't, then it is also my duty to tell them if you have not"* *"You do know why I must do this, don't you?"* *"I'm sure you'll understand my concerns that you could seriously injure yourself or others at work or on the road"* *"Once you are well and on a stable routine of medication, you should be able to regain your freedom"*

Key points to cover (continued)   **Example phrases (continued)**

Offer to make enquiries regarding disability living allowance

"In the meantime, I can find out what support in terms of 'financial support' you can claim for"

Mention support groups (e.g. Epilepsy Society). Offer the opportunity to take information leaflets

Ask if there are further questions and close (by scheduling a follow-up if appropriate)

ISCMEDICAL
Interview Skills Consulting

8 | SERIOUS COMPLICATION
Doctor's Brief: Page 13   Patient's Brief: Page 39

Key points to cover	Example phrases
Listen actively to the son's concerns: • The diagnosis of necrotising fasciitis • Concern about the father's prognosis • Complaint about the complication not discussed in the consent	*"I am interested in finding out what you know so far about your father's condition?"*
Demonstrate empathy: • Put yourself in the son's place • Understand his worry for his father • Understand how powerless and uninformed he feels	*"I can understand it was a difficult time for your family when your father contracted this unusual complication of surgery"*
Convey with clarity: • The complication of necrotising fasciitis is rare • Precautions were taken to prevent infections • Difficulties in recognising the condition in early stages	*"I hope you understand that the complication is very rare and that all the necessary measures were taken to prevent this from happening"*
Demonstrate that the son understands the issues	*"I have mentioned a lot of things. Do you feel you have a better picture of what has happened and the way things are going now?"*

Interview Skills Consulting

Suggested Approach

Key points to cover (continued)	**Example phrases (continued)**
Your desire to keep them informed of the patient's progress	*"Indeed, this is a serious complication of diabetes. However, please be assured that I will continue to be in touch with the hospital to make sure that he receives the highest standard of care. We will also keep you informed of any news"*
Offer the opportunity to lodge a complaint if conflict continues	
Ask if there is anything further that he wishes to clarify and offer a meeting with him and other family members if desired	

9	LATE COMPLICATION
	Doctor's Brief: Page 14 Patient's Brief: Page 40

Key points to cover	**Example phrases**
Listen actively to the patient's concerns: • The impact on quality of life • The coping strategies • Why he has declined the further treatments • Suggestions of suicidal thoughts	*"I understand that you are going through a hard time dealing with the complications of the prostate operation. I'd like to take some time to discuss all your concerns"* *"I can imagine how these problems must be getting to you. Have you ever thought it was all too much for you?"*
Demonstrate empathy: • Put yourself in the patient's place	
Convey with clarity: • The complications of TURP • Precautions were taken to prevent such complications • Possibilities of a second opinion for further treatment • Possibility of drug assisted erection	
Convey your desire to keep giving medical and emotional support. In particular, express your concern over his emotional fragility.	*"I can sense that you are emotionally very fragile and showing early symptoms of depression. I would like to take an active role in giving you more support with your emotions"*

Key points to cover (continued)	Example phrases (continued)
	"It's very unfortunate that the complications you experience are very private but have a huge impact on your quality of life. I want you to know that, as your doctor, I am here to give you support to help overcome these difficult problems"
Demonstrate patient understanding of the issues	
Offer the opportunity to take information leaflets or details of support groups if appropriate	
Ask if there are further questions and close (by scheduling a follow-up if appropriate)	

10 | INTERNET MEDICINE

Doctor's Brief: Page 15   Patient's Brief: Page 41

Key points to cover	Example phrases
Listen actively to the patient's concerns: • The impact of the mole on her quality of life • Her understanding of the laser treatment	*"How does this mole affect your life?"* *"What sort of expectations do you have from this new treatment?"*
Demonstrate empathy: • Put yourself in the patient's place • Understand how this mole makes her feel	*"I understand that you are obviously not happy, that you are concerned with the look of this mole and this makes you keen to participate in new treatments like this laser technology. However..."*
Convey with clarity: • The complications of laser treatment may be undesirable • The minimal scientific data • The possibility that the patient may need to self-fund the treatment • Possibility of second opinion and alternative therapies	*"I can see why these new therapies look appealing but there really isn't a lot of unbiased evidence of success beyond the commercial claims. In fact there is a strong possibility that these treatments can do more harm than good"* *"I hope you can have the opportunity to discuss the options of surgery with our well-trusted and experienced clinicians such as plastic surgeons rather than a beauty therapist. Perhaps they can reassure you regarding your fear of surgery"*

Key points to cover (continued)	**Example phrases (continued)**
Offer to do some investigation first before she pursues treatment further	*"Would you allow me to make some enquiries before you take things further? I really worry that you might put yourself at risk and I can find out more about these techniques from some colleagues"*
Demonstrate patient understanding of the issues	*"After our conversation, I hope you understand why I would rather you reconsider this treatment. Can you see why I have concerns?"*
Express your desire to keep giving medical and emotional support. You may offer counselling	*"We have discussed a lot including other options for treating you. I am happy to continue seeing you and we can discuss these things after you have had more thought, but overall I do want you to know that I want to help you with this"* *"In the meantime would you like to talk to one of my colleagues? She helps people talk though things, like a counsellor. You can give it a go and see how you get on"*
Ask if there are further questions and close (by scheduling a follow-up if appropriate)	

11 RESOURCE RATIONING – IVF

| Doctor's Brief: Page 16 | Patient's Brief: Page 42 |

Key points to cover

Example phrases

Listen actively to the patient's concerns:
- The impact of infertility on her quality of life
- The unfair distribution of resources

"I understand the difficult time you are experiencing with infertility problems, and how disappointed you must be that your application has been declined"

Demonstrate empathy:
- Put yourself in the patient's place

"I have the impression that you are extremely unhappy and feel let down by us, because of the fact that your neighbours' application has just been approved"

Convey with clarity:
- The selection criteria of IVF treatment
- The limited resources in the PCT for such treatment
- The possibility for younger patients to make further applications
- The possibility of appeal

"I hope you understand that every case is different and I am sure you also understand that I cannot discuss other patients' applications with you. Please be assured that, although it may not seem that way, the selection mechanism is fair"

Demonstrate that the patient has understood these issues

"Now that I have explained a bit more about the process, do you understand why the application has gone this way?"

Key points to cover (continued)   **Example phrases (continued)**

Offer the opportunity to take information
leaflets or details of support groups if
appropriate

Ask if there are further questions and close
(by scheduling a follow-up if appropriate)

Express your desire to keep giving medical   *"As your GP, I am here to*
and emotional support, including about   *assist you in whatever way is*
marital difficulties   *possible. If you feel that this is*
                                                affecting your relationship too
                                                much, I may be able to put you
                                                in touch with a counsellor who
                                                could talk things through with
                                                you"

12 | OBESITY AND ITS CONSEQUENCES

| Doctor's Brief: Page 17 | Patient's Brief: Page 43 |

Key points to cover

Example phrases

Listen actively to the patient's concerns:
- The impact of the pain on her quality of life
- The patient's dissatisfaction with the description of obesity

"I know that you are upset because you are not having the operation. I would like to discuss these concerns with you"

Demonstrate empathy:
- Put yourself in the patient's place
- Understand how the pain may affect her life
- Acknowledge the insensitivity of the word "obese"

"I understand it is insensitive of the hospital not to take into account the attempts that you have made to reduce weight"

"I know you were offended by the word 'obese' and I apologise for the insensitivity of this"

Convey with clarity:
- The selection criteria for total hip replacement
- The limited life span of the hip and high complications
- Potential further options to facilitate and support weight loss
- Possibility of second opinion

"Although it may seem like an unjust and sweeping decision, there may be reasons behind the refusal for surgery that they didn't fully explain to you. For instance, did you know that some of these artificial hips don't last very long and may need to be replaced?...which would really be a waste of your time"

Key points to cover (continued)	**Example phrases (continued)**
Explore the possibility of better and alternative options for pain control	*"I hope that after today's conversation you understand why we should move forward and work towards the objectives of helping you lose weight and control the pain"*
Demonstrate that the patient has understood these issues	
Express your desire to keep giving medical and emotional support	*"I wish to continue to be part of your health care and give you the attention and support that you need"*
Offer the opportunity to take information leaflets or details of support groups if appropriate	
Ask if there are further questions and close (by scheduling a follow-up if appropriate)	

13 COMPLICATIONS OF CHRONIC THERAPY
Doctor's Brief: Page 18   Patient's Brief: Page 44

Key points to cover	Example phrases
Listen actively to the patient's concerns:	

Listen actively to the patient's concerns:
- The impact of asthma on quality of life
- The impact of the pain on quality of life
- Patient dissatisfaction with the high dose steroid and its complications
- Patient's disappointment at being refused surgery despite the obesity being due to his steroid treatment

Demonstrate empathy:
- Put yourself in the patient's situation
- Acknowledge the patient's disappointment with the complications

"I understand the reason for your weight gain is solely medical. I am sorry how the steroids have affected you to this extent"

"I can sense your dissatisfaction and anger with the treatment which has caused you all these problems"

Convey with clarity:
- The necessity of steroids in asthma management
- The unfortunate complications of steroid and refusal of surgery
- Possibility to reduce steroid intake and alternative treatments in conjunction with the specialists
- Possibility of second opinion for his hip problem

"I hope you understand the intention of the steroid treatment in the first place"

"I know that right now it all seems to have gone wrong and you would have been better off without the steroids. What I can tell you is that without them you may have been critically unwell with your asthma but in time we can help you with these side effects"

Key points to cover (continued)	Example phrases (continued)
Explore the possibility of better pain control	*"Surgery is not the be all and end all of options. There are many other things we can try"*
Demonstrate that the patient has understood these issues	*"I know that you are eager to reverse all these side effects by stopping the medication, but do you understand the importance of working with me in order to avoid life-threatening consequences of stopping the steroid yourself?"*
Express your desire to keep giving medical and emotional support	
Offer the opportunity to take information leaflets or details of support groups if appropriate	
Ask if there are further questions and close (by scheduling a follow-up if appropriate)	

"iSCMEDICAL
Interview Skills Consulting

14	FEAR OF CANCER
	Doctor's Brief: Page 19 Patient's Brief: Page 45

Key points to cover

Example phrases

Listen actively to the patient's concerns:
- The impact of the loss of his father
- Anxiety of prostate cancer
- Patient's quality of life

"I am sorry to hear about the loss of your father. I hope to take this opportunity to help and support you through this difficult time"

Demonstrate empathy:
- Put yourself in the patient's place
- Acknowledge the bereavement and anxiety

"Family bereavement is difficult enough for you and your family. However, I sense that you are obviously concerned about the potential impact of cancer on yourself in the future. Please let me help you, and we can work together to manage this"

Explore the symptoms to determine if they are related to anxiety or bereavement
Evaluate any suicidal ideation

"I realise these changes to your life are not normal for you. Have you ever come to a point when you thought it's all too much? Have you ever thought it is not worth going on any more?"

Convey with clarity:
- The concern you and his family have over his symptoms
- Highlight the effectiveness of early detection and cure of cancer

Key points to cover (continued)	**Example phrases (continued)**
Offer opportunity for bereavement counselling	
Express your desire to keep giving medical and emotional support	
Offer the opportunity to take information leaflets or details of support groups if appropriate	
Ask if there are further questions and close (by scheduling a follow-up if appropriate)	

ISCMEDICAL
Interview Skills Consulting

15	LATE FAILURE OF VASECTOMY
	Doctor's Brief: Page 20 Patient's Brief: Page 46

Key points to cover

Example phrases

Listen actively to the patient's concerns:
- The impact of this incident on his marriage
- Anger he has regarding the complications not explained in the initial consent
- Impact this pregnancy has on his and his wife's life

"I understand how these events have created a lot of confusion and uncertainty in the family. Can you please tell me how this has affected your relationship and any concerns you have about coping with another child in the family?"

Demonstrate empathy:
- Put yourself in the patient's place
- Acknowledge the anger, disappointment and anxiety for the future

"I can understand why you are upset with the situation and the impact it has on you and your wife. I can also relate to you regarding how to cope with another pregnancy at this stage of your life"

Convey with clarity:
- Apologise for the complication not being discussed explicitly before
- Apologise for any problems this may have caused in the marital relationship
- Discuss the options of termination of pregnancy

"I sincerely apologise for not discussing such complications with you before the operation. This is indeed an extremely rare complication and it is not often mentioned explicitly. For that, I am sorry"

Demonstrate that the patient has understood these issues

"I hope you have understood how we have come to this situation, and what options lie ahead. Would you tell me what you have gathered from this conversation and how you want to move forward?"

Key points to cover (continued)	Example phrases (continued)
Offer the opportunity to make a complaint	*"I do understand you may still feel strongly about the situation and of course you can lodge a formal complaint if you wish"*
Mention your desire to keep giving medical and emotional support	
Ask if there are further questions and close (by scheduling a follow-up if appropriate)	

16	MIX-UP WITH RESULTS
	Doctor's Brief: Page 21 Patient's Brief: Page 47

Key points to cover	Example phrases
Apologise and clarify the situation (it may be best to begin with this)	*"Firstly I have good news for you: that the breast lump we removed was completely benign, as in normal. A dreadful mix-up occurred with another patient and we sincerely apologise to you for this dreadful mistake"*
Listen actively to the patient's concerns: ▪ The impact of the bad news and the anxiety it has caused ▪ The anger experienced by the patient as a result of the mix-up ▪ The patient's quality of life ▪ The relief of the good news	*"I am sorry you had to go through the anguish of getting the wrong results and hope I can help you to get over the shock"* *"Tell me...what has been happening in the last few weeks since you got the early result? You must have had a lot to go through"*
Demonstrate empathy: ▪ Put yourself in the patient's place ▪ Acknowledge the severity of the error	*"I can see how angry you are with the mix-up, and of course you have all the right to be angry. I can understand how this has had devastating effects on you and your family"*

Key points to cover (continued)
Convey with clarity:
- How easily mistakes can happen but this is no excuse
- The concerns that you have with the mix-up

Example phrases (continued)
"I hope you understand how mistakes can happen, but this is no excuse. I am taking this very seriously and will take appropriate action to report this

---

- Ask the patient to focus on the good news now
- The measure you will take to ensure no such future mistake (incident reporting, etc) occurs

incident so that it is formally looked into and similar mistakes can be avoided in the future"

Demonstrate patient understanding of how the mistake could happen

"I hope you can accept my apology and you can now look at the positive side of this episode, which is the fact that you are clear of cancer"

Offer the opportunity to lodge a complaint

"I can understand if you are still upset, and I offer you an opportunity to lodge a formal complaint if you wish to do so"

Mention your desire to keep giving medical and emotional support

"I also understand you may have lost faith in this hospital. I am happy to put you in touch with another hospital for a future follow-up and even for a second opinion if you wish"

Ask if there are further questions and close (by scheduling a follow-up if appropriate)

<table>
<tr><td rowspan="2">**17**</td><td colspan="2">**RESPONSE TO BEREAVEMENT**</td></tr>
<tr><td>Doctor's Brief: Page 22</td><td>Patient's Brief: Page 48</td></tr>
</table>

RESPONSE TO BEREAVEMENT

17   Doctor's Brief: Page 22   Patient's Brief: Page 48

Key points to cover	**Example phrases**
Listen actively to the patient's concerns: • The impact of the loss of her mother • Anxiety of breast cancer • Patient's quality of life • Explore any suicidal thoughts	*"I am sorry for your loss. I understand she was so young and you were both very close. Can you please tell me your thoughts and concerns?"*
Demonstrate empathy: • Put yourself in the patient's place • Acknowledge the bereavement and anxiety	*"I understand it is a very difficult time for you at the moment. Apart from dealing with your loss, I can sense you are rather worried the loss has affected you adversely. I can detect symptoms of anxiety in our conversation"*
Convey with clarity: • The concern you and her family have over her problems • The effectiveness of screening for breast cancer, its early detection and cure • The irrational decision for surgery at this stage • The impact of prophylactic mastectomies on her future life	*"I can see your viewpoint in taking measures to prevent the occurrence of cancer; however, I think the decision you have made is rather hasty. I urge you to take some more time to think over this decision, maybe when your mind has settled a little. Things are very fresh for you at the moment and it can be difficult to see your way through it all right now. You might look back at this in a short while and realise you have made a bad decision"*

Key points to cover (continued)	Example phrases (continued)
Demonstrate that the patient has understood these issues	*"I hope you have understood what we discussed today, and I would like to see you again soon to discuss this in more detail. Can you tell me what your thoughts are at the moment?"*
Offer opportunity for bereavement counselling and to investigate a referral to a genetic counsellor	*"I am not ignoring your concerns, they are very important and, because of that, I'd like to refer you to a few people who can help. Someone to help you think through all of this and also a specialist in cancers who may be able to see if there is a 'family link' to you"*
Mention your desire to keep giving medical and emotional support	*"I would like you to know that, as your GP, my role is to provide you with the necessary support to overcome this very difficult period of your life"*
Offer the opportunity to take information leaflets or details of support groups if appropriate	
Ask if there are further questions and close (by scheduling a follow-up if appropriate)	

18	**A SCEPTICAL PATIENT – MMR**	
	Doctor's Brief: Page 23	Patient's Brief: Page 49

Key points to cover

Listen actively to the patient's concerns:
- Anxiety over MMR
- Feelings of discrimination due to social status

Demonstrate empathy:
- Put yourself in the patient's place
- Acknowledge the anxiety and disappointment

Convey with clarity:
- The importance of vaccinations
- The lack of robust evidence to associate MMR with autism
- Highlight the devastation of measles, mumps and rubella

State your desire to keep giving medical and emotional support

Example phrases

"I understand that Johnny has not had his vaccinations. Would you like to discuss your concerns with me regarding this?"

"As a parent myself, I understand the anguish and fear that you have. I can also see some degree of anger you have towards the health service for not being able to provide the alternative vaccinations"

"I can tell you that there is no firm evidence to relate MMR to autism at present. I understand it is a difficult decision to make. However, for the safety of your son, I strongly suggest that he has the vaccine. If unprotected, he is at risk of measles and the consequences of this disease may be devastating"

Key points to cover (continued)	Example phrases (continued)
Demonstrate that the patient has understood these issues	*"I hope you understand my concerns with your child's well being, and please understand why the health service cannot provide the alternative vaccinations due to lack of scientific evidence. Do you understand?"*
Offer the opportunity to see a specialist	*"I would really like you to re-consider your decision and I am prepared to put you in touch with a paediatric specialist who can tell you more about the safety of the MMR vaccine"*
Ask if there are further questions and close (by scheduling a follow-up if appropriate)	

ISCMEDICAL
Interview Skills Consulting

19 | SELF-FUNDED TREATMENT
Doctor's Brief: Page 24   Patient's Brief: Page 50

Key points to cover	Example phrases
Listen actively to the son's concerns: • The self-funding and financial situation that his mother has got into • The non-effectiveness of the medication	*"Can you tell me what you have learnt about your mother's condition, her treatment, and the funding of this treatment?"*
Demonstrate empathy: • Put yourself in the son's place • Acknowledge the anger, disappointment and frustration	*"As a member of a close family, like yours, I can relate to your anger and disappointment when you found out that you would need to fund this treatment by yourself"*
Convey with clarity: • The basis of the agreed terms of prescription • The treatment is still under assessment and may become formulary approved • Declare your lack of awareness regarding the sale of her property	*"I do apologise for the misunderstanding. I can assure you that I had no prior knowledge of her methods for funding the treatment. I am also concerned that she has suffered as a consequence of making these funds available"*
Demonstrate that the son has understood these issues	
Offer opportunity to see the patient and son together	*"I hope you understand that I cannot discuss the details of her condition with you. The best thing to do may be to ask her to attend the clinic with you on another occasion"*

Key points to cover (continued)	Example phrases (continued)
State your desire to keep giving medical and emotional support	
Ask if there are further questions and close (by scheduling a follow-up if appropriate)	

20	**PRESUMED MALTREATMENT**	
	Doctor's Brief: Page 25	Patient's Brief: Page 51

Key points to cover	**Example phrases**
Listen actively to the son's concerns: • About the bruises • Reasons for the suspected abuse • These "accidents" are recurrent	*"I understand you have concerns regarding your mother's recurrent accidents and the bruises that she has. I am keen to listen to these concerns and work through them with you"*
Demonstrate empathy: • Put yourself in the son's place • Acknowledge the son's concerns	*"I totally understand why you are concerned about possible abuse and your mother's safety in hospital"*
Convey with clarity: • Your involvement with the patient around these accidents • Explain that you are taking these concerns seriously and that you will investigate them appropriately • Explain how documentation and procedures lead you to believe she is in safe hands • Reassure patient's son that all measures will be taken to prevent future recurrence	*"I can assure you that I have personally attended to your mother on previous occasions when she had the falls and I have never come across anything to lead me to believe they were anything but accidental. Of course I take your concerns seriously and I will investigate accordingly"* *"In fact, whenever patients fall like this, a formal report is filled in. I can go through some of these with you and I think you will see the circumstances surrounding these falls may well have been unavoidable"*

Key points to cover (continued)	Example phrases (continued)
Demonstrate that the patient's son has understood these issues	*"I hope you understand the previous falls have all been documented and all measures have been taken to ensure her safety"*
Offer the opportunity for the son to participate in the patient's future management plans	*"I'd like to continue to keep you up to date with our progress and involve you in future planning for your mother"*
State your desire to keep giving medical and emotional support	
Ask if there are further questions and close (by scheduling a follow-up if appropriate)	

ISCMEDICAL
Interview Skills Consulting

21	**FRASER GUIDELINES**
	Doctor's Brief: Page 26 Patient's Brief: Page 52

Key points to cover | **Example phrases**

Listen actively to the mother's concerns:
- About the child's safety
- About Anna's sexual partner
- About possible child abuse
- Anger about being left out of the decision making and knowledge regarding her daughter

"What has led you to have worries about Anna?"

"Do you have any particular worries about her?"

Demonstrate empathy:
- Put yourself in the mother's place
- Acknowledge the anger, disappointment and fears

"I fully appreciate the issues that you are concerned about. I understand why you are angry and anxious. I also know it can be frustrating when you feel you are being left in the dark about it all"

Convey with clarity:
- Child protection is of paramount importance and you act by what is felt best for the child
- Encourage the mother to come with Anna
- Explain that medico-legally Anna is capable of making these decisions

Above all retain confidentiality to Anna – do not disclose any information that may be personal to Anna

"As Anna's GP, I have a duty to maintain confidentiality to her just as I keep confidentiality of all my patients including you. For that reason I can't discuss any medical details of what has been happening without her consent. I am really sorry that is the way it is and I know how frustrating this seems, but these are principles that all doctors work by. What I can say, however, is that, when dealing with issues relating to a young person, we work using strict guidance to make sure that we take the safety of children as

Key points to cover (continued)	Example phrases (continued)
	our first concern, above anything else, and, to that end, any dealings with your daughter would have involved us securing her personal safety if that were at risk, and going to whatever lengths were necessary to protect her"
Demonstrate that the mother has understood (if not agrees with) these issues	*"There are so many reasons why it is best to maintain confidentiality and trust, even with those under 18. I hope you realise that we are acting in what we believe to be her best interests and would not let any harm come to her"*
Offer opportunity to see both Anna and her mother together at some time	*"I can see you also want the best for her and as part of my role as her doctor I will continue to encourage her to get you involved with her decisions. I will encourage her to bring you along next time she comes so that we can all work together to give her the support she needs"*
Ask if there are further questions and close (by scheduling a follow-up if appropriate)	

22	**SUBSTANCE ABUSE**	
	Doctor's Brief: Page 27	Patient's Brief: Page 53

Key points to cover

Example phrases

Listen actively to the patient's concerns:
- Fear of isolation
- Fear of losing his children
- Feeling of low self-esteem and self-worth
- Explore any suicidal ideation
- Desire to get on with life
- Fear of loss of control with his drinking

"I see from your notes that you have had a lot to deal with lately. Please tell me more about how you have been coping"

"You seem to be afraid of some things in life…"

"Do you think deep down that you want to move on from all of this?"

Demonstrate empathy:
- Put yourself in the patient's place
- Acknowledge his fears regarding losing his daughters
- Acknowledge his low self-worth
- Acknowledge his alcohol problem and fear of losing control

"I think anyone in your position would feel the same"

"You have done well to cope until now. Don't be so hard on yourself"

"It must all seem very difficult to handle at the moment; your morale must be very low"

Convey with clarity:
- The need to turn his life around and stop drinking
- The importance of his physical and mental health in his fight for his children
- Further benzodiazepines may be habit-forming and are not a good idea

"It is very easy to escape into drink, but I know that deep down you also believe you can come out of this and build a future. You do have your children to think of. Your ability to get fair custody will be badly affected if you continue on this course"

Key points to cover (continued)	Example phrases (continued)
Offer him the opportunity to: • See you on a regular basis • See a counsellor • Get independent support regarding his divorce • Get involved with support groups	*"I would like to see you more regularly to support you, but I wonder if you would consider seeing one of my colleagues... she is a counsellor...she can listen to you and help you make strides forward in your life"*
Demonstrate that the patient has understood these issues	*"Do you see why I am reluctant to prescribe you more tablets?"*
Reiterate your desire to keep giving medical and emotional support	
Offer the opportunity to take information leaflets or details of support groups if appropriate	
Ask if there are further questions and close (by scheduling a follow-up if appropriate)	

23 SUPPORT FOR PARENTS

Doctor's Brief: Page 28   Patient's Brief: Page 54

Key points to cover

Example phrases

Explain the purpose of the visit

"Thank you for coming to see me about Clare. As her doctor, I am somewhat concerned with recent events which have led to her falls. I may be over cautious, but I would like to make sure Clare has not had any difficulties at school with other children"

Listen actively to the mother's concerns:
- About the child's recurrent falls
- Previous records of bullying
- Child's school performance and friends
- Other telltale signs of bullying

"I wonder if you can tell me any concerns you have about the falls and any other changes in behaviour she is showing"

Demonstrate empathy:
- Put yourself in the mother's/father's place
- Acknowledge the anxiety and anguish over the child's well-being
- Reassure the mother/father that she should not feel responsible for the bullying but emphasise the need to address the issue proactively

"I know you probably didn't think the falls were suspicious. However, for Clare's safety, I think we must take action to make sure bullying isn't happening at school"

"I fully understand your concerns and anguish. It must be difficult to deal with this issue as a parent"

Key points to cover (continued)	Example phrases (continued)
Convey with clarity: ■ Highlight the necessity for further investigations for the child's safety ■ Encourage the mother/father to come with the child	*"Our top priority is Clare's well-being. Therefore, I suggest that we make another appointment with Clare so that we can tackle this sensitive issue together"*
Demonstrate that the mother/father understands these issues	*"I hope you understand my suspicions and why I want to see you all"*
Your desire to keep giving medical and emotional support	
Offer the opportunity to take information leaflets or details of support groups if appropriate	
Ask if there are further questions and close (by scheduling a follow-up if appropriate)	

24 PARENTAL SEPARATION & THE CHILD
Doctor's Brief: Page 29   Patient's Brief: Page 55

Key points to cover	Example phrases
Explain the purpose of the consultation	*"I have noticed Peter has not been very happy lately. I am concerned that he is losing weight and seems a bit withdrawn. Have you noticed anything like this lately?"*
Listen actively to the father's/mother's concerns: • The emotional impact of the separation • Peter's school performance and friends • Other telltale signs of depression	*"I appreciate this is a very difficult time you are having. You need to be strong both for yourself and your family"* *"Apart from the impact this has on your own health, I also worry about how the separation may be affecting your children"*
Demonstrate empathy: • Put yourself in the father's/mother' place • Acknowledge the anxiety and anguish over the child	*"I can only imagine all the difficulties you are facing at the moment dealing with the separation. It must be extremely difficult to cope with the present situation"*
Convey with clarity: • The necessity to think of the child's interests • Encourage the father/mother to come with the child	*"I would like you to know that my role is to give you full support to get through this difficult period. I suggest that we should arrange to see you and Peter together so that you can give each other strength and support"*

Key points to cover (continued)

Example phrases (continued)

Key points to cover (continued)	Example phrases (continued)
Demonstrate that the father has understood these issues	*"I don't want you to feel that I am putting extra pressure on you. On the contrary, I am here to help you and Peter. Can you see that?"*
Mention your desire to keep giving medical and emotional support	
Offer the opportunity to take information leaflets or details of support groups if appropriate	
Ask if there are further questions and close (by scheduling a follow-up if appropriate)	

OTHER BOOKS IN THIS SERIES

GP RECRUITMENT STAGE 2

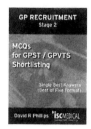
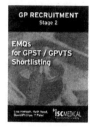

GP RECRUITMENT STAGE 3

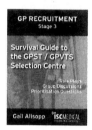

OTHER BOOKS SUITABLE FOR REVISION

SEE OUR WEBSITE FOR FULL DETAILS
WWW.ISCMEDICAL.CO.UK